سُنو سُنو

Listen, Listen

written by Phillis Gershator
illustrated by Alison Jay

Urdu translation by Qamar Zamani

سُنو، سُنو۔۔۔ وہ آواز کیا ہے؟ کیڑے چاروں طرف گانا گا رہے ہیں!

Listen, listen ... what's that sound? Insects singing all around!

پُوں، پُوں، چیں، چیں، بڑ، بڑ، وھر، وھر۔

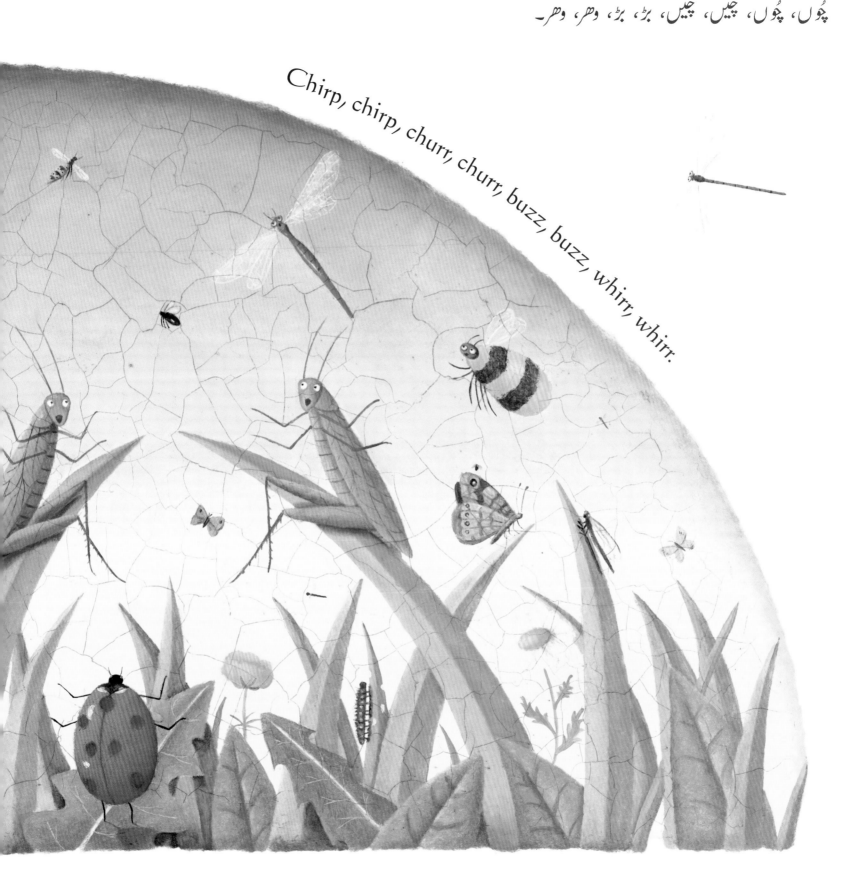

Chirp, chirp, churr, churr, buzz, buzz, whirr whirr.

پتّے سرسراتے ہیں۔ جھولے کے پلنگ ہچکولے کھاتے ہیں۔ چھپ چھپ، بچے جھاگ اُڑاتے ہیں۔

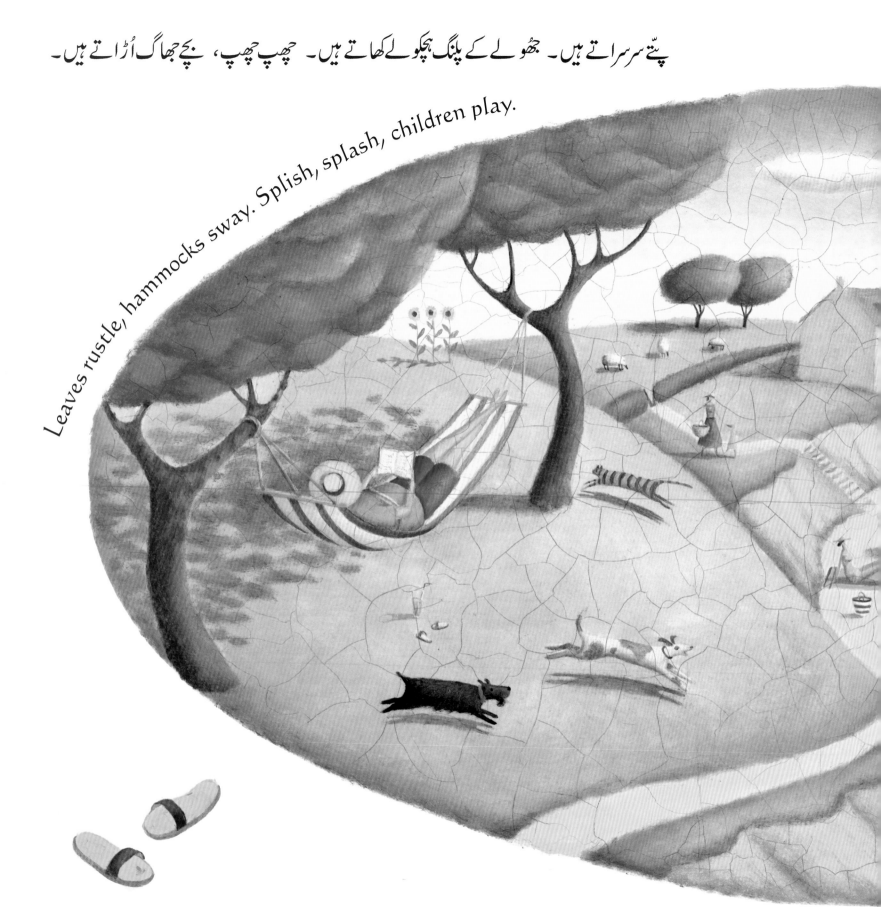

Leaves rustle, hammocks sway. Splish, splash, children play.

بادل اِدھر اُدھر ڈولتے ہیں، کُتّے دوڑتے ہیں۔ گرمیوں کا جلتا سورج چھن چھن کرتا ہے۔

Clouds drift, dogs run. Sizzle, sizzle, summer sun.

سُنو، سُنو ۔۔۔گرمیاں گزر گئیں۔ خدا حافظ کیڑو، خزاں کا موسم آ گیا۔

Listen, listen ... summer's gone.
Good-bye insects, autumn's come.

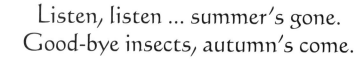

ٹپ، ٹپ، شاہ بلوط کے پھل ٹپکتے ہیں۔ جلدی، جلدی، سٹر پٹر گلہریاں اُنہیں پکڑنے پھدکتی ہیں۔

Plop, plop, acorns drop.
Hurry, scurry, squirrels hop.

کدّو پکتے ہیں، جلدی، جلدی، جلدی۔ سیب اور بھٹّے۔ چُن لو، چُن لو۔

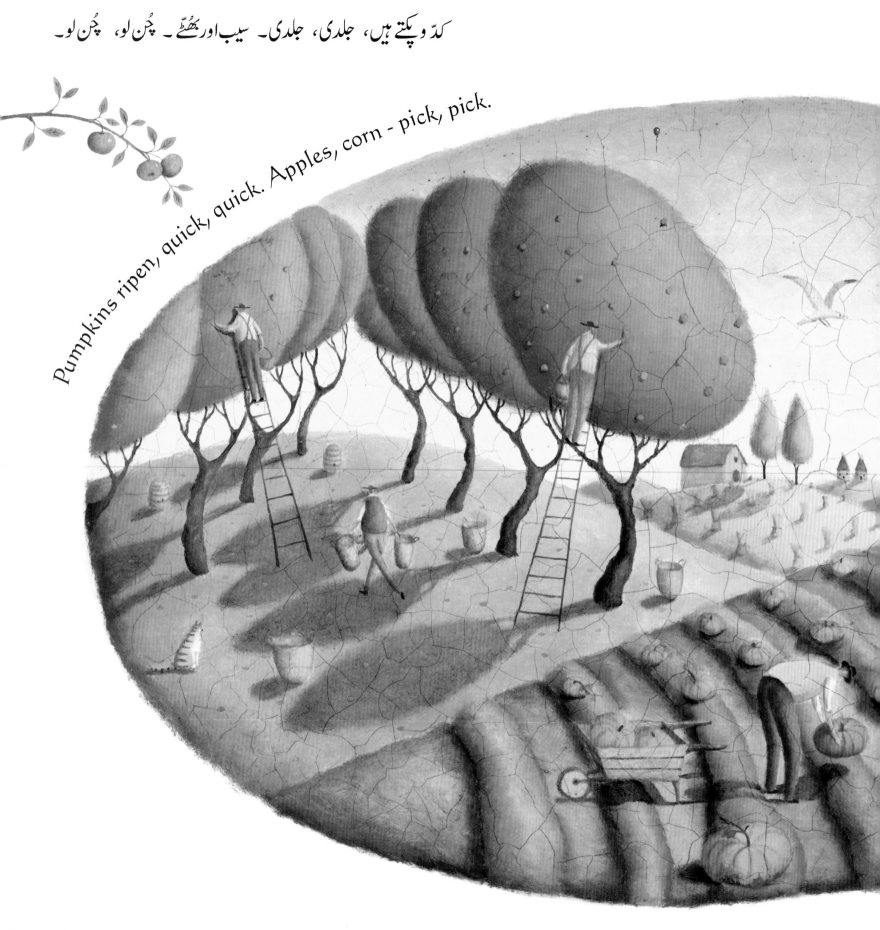

Pumpkins ripen, quick, quick. Apples, corn - pick, pick.

کچر کچر کی آواز کے ساتھ لوگ چلتے ہیں۔ قیں، قیں، آبی مرغابیاں پکارتی ہیں۔

Crunch, crunch, people walk. Aak, aak, seagulls squawk.

تیز آواز سے بطخیں چلّاتی ہیں۔ شرر، شرر، پتّے گرتے ہیں۔

Honk, honk, geese call. Swish, swish, leaves fall.

شُوں، شاں، ہیٹ اُڑتے ہیں۔ ہُو ہُو، اُلّو چیختے ہیں۔

Whoosh, whoosh, hats fly. Whoo, whoo, owls cry.

سُنو، سُنو ۔۔۔خزاں کا موسم گزر گیا۔ برف کے گالے سرگوشیاں کرتے ہیں ''جاڑوں میں بہت مزہ آتا ہے۔''

Listen, listen ... autumn's gone. Snowflakes whisper, "Winter's fun."

چپ چاپ، برفیلی رات۔ برف جگمگاتی ہے، سفید اور چمکیلی۔

Shhh, shhh, snowy night. Snow sparkles, white, bright.

کچر، کچر، بوٹ دھماکے دار آواز نکالتے ہیں۔ بڑے لوگ زمین پر برف کھودتے ہیں اور بچے دھاچوکڑی مچاتے ہیں۔

Crunch, crunch, boots clomp. Grown-ups shovel, children romp.

برف پر تختہ رانی کرنے والے چکر کاٹتے ہیں۔ دھاردار جوتوں والے برف پر پھسلتے ہیں۔ زَن، زَن۔

Skaters spin, skiers glide. Zip, zoom, slip, slide.

برر، برر، گرم ہونے کا وقت۔ آہا، آہا، موم بتیاں چمکتی ہیں۔

Brrr, brrr, warm-up time. Ooh, aah, candles shine.

خر، خر، بلیاں ٹکٹکی باندھ کر دیکھتی ہیں، چٹر، پٹر، شعلے بھڑکتے ہیں۔

Purr, purr, cats gaze. Crackle, crackle, fires blaze.

سُنو، سُنو۔۔۔ جاڑوں کا موسم گزر گیا۔ زرد چونچ والی چڑیاں سیٹی بجاتی ہیں۔ ''دیکھو سورج نکل آیا!''

Listen, listen ... winter's gone. Finches whistle, "Here's the sun!"

پَٹ، پَٹ، کونپلیں پھوٹتی ہیں۔ پتّے لہراتے ہیں۔ رنگ برنگے پھول کھلکھلاتے ہیں۔

Pop, pop, bulbs sprout. Leaves grow, flowers shout.

چِک، چِک، چوزے نکلتے ہیں۔ چُوں، چُوں، چوزے مٹی کھرچتے ہیں۔

Crick, crack, babies hatch. Peep, peep, chickens scratch.

میینڈک ٹرّاتے ہیں۔ بطخیں تیز آواز نکالتی ہیں۔ کچر، کچر، خرگوش گاجر کھاتے ہیں۔

Frogs croak, ducklings quack. Munch, munch, rabbits snack.

بارش ہوتی ہے، رِم جھِم رِم جھِم۔ گوریّاں آپس میں بولتی ہیں، پُوں، پُوں، چِیں، چِیں، چِیں۔

Rains fall, pitter, patter. Sparrows gather, chitter, chatter.

سُنو، سُنو۔۔۔ بہار کا موسم گزر گیا۔ اَب ایک اور موسم شروع ہوا۔

Listen, listen ... spring is gone. Another season has begun.

ہواؤں میں، زمین پر، رات اور دن۔ یہ کیا آواز ہے؟

In the air, on the ground, night and day - what's that sound?

سُنو، سُنو.....بہار کے بعد گرمیوں کا موسم آتا ہے اور.....

Listen, listen ... after spring, summer comes and ...

کیڑے گانا گاتے ہیں!

Insects sing!

پُوں، پُوں، چیں، چیں، بڑ، بڑ، وھر، وھر۔

Chirp, chirp, churr, churr, buzz, buzz, whirr, whirr.

In the summer, can you see

a cricket

a butterfly

a mosquito

a bee

a dragonfly

a grasshopper

a beetle

a sunflower

a daisy

a leaf?

In the autumn, can you see

an owl

a goose

an acorn

an apple

a squirrel

a stalk of wheat

a pumpkin

an ear of corn

a seagull

a leaf?

In the winter, can you see

a crow

a mouse

a starling

a paw print

an icicle

a holly berry

a leaf?

a snowflake

a sprig of mistletoe

In the spring, can you see

tulip

a daffodil

a bluebell

a sparrow

a rainbow

a rabbit

a frog

a duckling

a chick

a leaf?

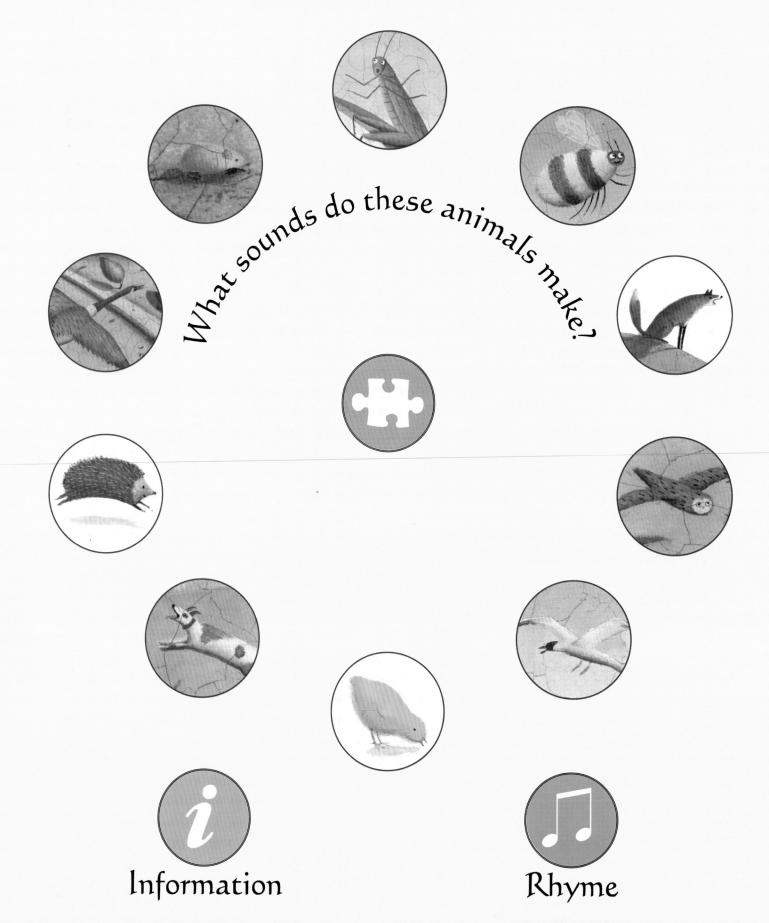

What sounds do these animals make?

Information

Rhyme